For Marcia & Nilda

First published 2016
Published by Butterfly Books Limited

A CIP catalogue record for this book is available from the British Library.

ISBN: 978-0-9932769-4-1

www.butterflybooks.uk

Edited by Corey Brotherson

Printed in England

My Mummy is a SCIENTIST

By Kerrine Bryan & Jason Bryan

Illustrated by Marissa Peguinho

My mummy is a scientist;
curious, keen and smart.

Her job is so exciting,
I don't know where to start.

From microscopes to telescopes,
the lab seems so much fun...
Test tubes, flasks and beakers,
we've only just begun.

Scientists explore the facts,
through different kinds of tests;
putting elements together,
to find out the effects.

My mummy is a scientist;
curious, keen and smart.
She knows all about the body,
and the workings of each part.

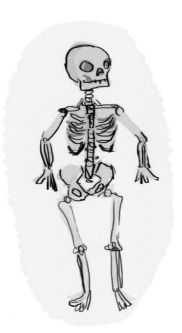
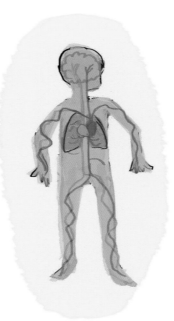
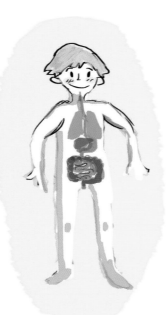

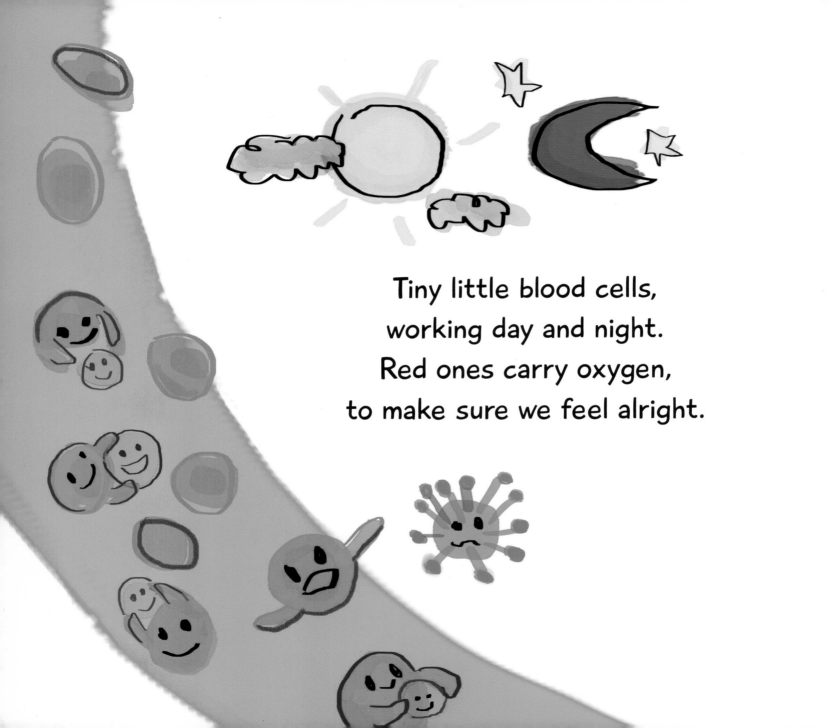

Tiny little blood cells,
working day and night.
Red ones carry oxygen,
to make sure we feel alright.

Scientists explore the facts,
so when we're feeling blue,
their tests can give them answers,
to know what they should do.

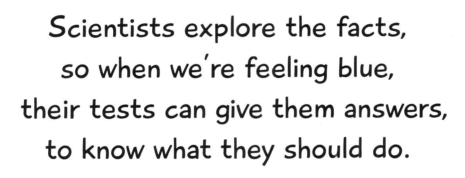

My mummy is a scientist;
curious, keen and smart.
She says that nature's wonderful:
it's like a work of art!

She knows how we get rain,
and also how it snows...

From earthquakes and hurricanes,
to raging volcanoes.

Scientists explore the facts,
like how the clouds can form,
and with this information,
they can predict a storm.

My mummy is a scientist;
curious, keen and smart.
She knows all about the planets...
The sun, the moon, the stars.

Scientists explore the facts,
they test and they observe;
so that one day in the future,
their work may save the world!

My mummy is a scientist;
curious, keen and smart.
My mummy is the greatest,
that's why she has my heart!